What Are You Rooted In?

Planting Seeds of Purpose

for

Anger

Workbook & Journal

ATHENA THOMAS

The Life Calling Coach
Live on purpose... Not by Accident

What Are You Rooted In?
Planting Seeds of Purpose for Anger
Workbook & Journal

ISBN: 9798682983902

Cover Design by Athena Thomas
Photos courtesy of Canva.com

Published by: The Life Calling Coach
www.thelifecallingcoach.com

Unless otherwise indicated, Scripture quotations are from:

The Holy Bible, New King James Version (NKJV) ©
The Message (MSG)
    Copyright © 1993, 1994, 1995, 1996, 2000,

2001, 2002 by Eugene H. Peterson

Dedication

This book series is dedicated to the friends lost to the destruction of their roots. My prayer is that this book may help at least one soul to survive and thrive in order to Live on Purpose.... Not By Accident!

Contents

Note to Readers

The scenarios in this book are based on my life. The journal entries are from my personal journals and help to tell my story. I have removed all names to protect the privacy of the people being mentioned throughout the book. I am not telling others' secrets only how my relationship with them has played out in my healing journey.

Some of the journal entries may contain scenarios that may be offensive. But they are necessary to reflect the true nature of the root issue being portrayed and the ultimate light that resulted in the healing journey. This book may not be for everyone but it is designed to meet those who need it where they are. For some, it may be while they you are living in that root issue.

I am a Spiritual Coach and refer to my Higher Power as "God" understanding that others refer to Him in different ways. In your journey you are encouraged to seek spiritual guidance through your established spiritual path. If you don't have one then this may open the door for you to plants seeds for spiritual growth and discover your Higher Power.

Foreword

Anger is not necessarily a "bad" emotion. Disrespect, rejection, injustice, racism, inequality, abuse, unemployment, illness, disease, death – all validly provokes anger within us. Anger can be the spark which fuels the necessary and positive changes needed within our society, community, family or self. Concern regarding your own anger may even be the reason you decided to pick up this workbook and start your own journey of healing.

Uncontrolled anger, however, can incite destruction within our society, community, family or self through outbreaks of verbal and physical aggression or violence. Denying anger is also harmful since it can lead to psychological symptoms such as depression and anxiety or somatic symptoms such as headaches, digestive difficulties, metabolism, Immune system difficulties, poor vision, lower bone density, high blood pressure, and heart disease. Anger also affects short-term memory and rational decision-making. That's why you may not be able to think or accurately remember what happened when angry[1] (NICABM, 2017).

My journey with healing contaminated roots of anger has been both personal and professional. Confronting my own anger has helped me become a better wife, mother and therapist. From personal experience, it may be a difficult journey. You may miss the mark from time to time and become discouraged. For that reason, I really encourage you to complete these exercises with an accountability partner, life coach, or therapist who can encourage you as well as gently point out your blind spots.

As a clinical social worker with over 30 years of experience, I have observed that hurting people can often see their faults, but have difficulty identifying their strengths. It is so important that while identifying the roots of your anger, you also identify the Strength (Higher Power) or strengths (within you) that have upheld you. If you have developed destructive patterns in coping with your anger, it is so very important that you not only stop these destructive patterns but also replace them with healthy

---

[1] The National Institute for the Clinical Application of Behavioral Medicine. (2017). *How Anger Affects Your Brain and Body.* Storrs, CT, United States. https://www.iahe.com/docs/articles/nicabm-anger-infographic-printable-pdf.pdf

coping skills. It will take time, patience, and practice for these healthy patterns to be your new norm. Try to celebrate each victory and don't become frustrated with each setback.

It is also very important to recognize that you may become triggered during your journey. If, while working on these exercises, you find that you are becoming angrier, depressed, anxious, or irritable, please seek professional help. Seeking professional help is not a sign of weakness, but may be necessary to maximize your personal growth. Contaminated roots of anger can be deep and/or complicated which may be difficult to entangle alone. Professional therapists have training and experience in addressing anger and can equip you with additional coping strategies necessary for your healing journey.

I am so excited that Coach Athena decided to lead you in this healing journey which will enable you to **SEE** the spiritual roots of anger in your life and willingly release them, **ACCEPT** their presence in your life, and **AGREE** that they have caused stagnation to self and others. I am also excited that **YOU** have decided to take this journey. It's a journey that hopefully will not end as you finish this workbook, but one that will continue throughout your life.

Cynthia Becker, LCSW-C, Clinical Social Worker, Support By Design Therapy Group

Introduction

What Are You Rooted In? Planting Seeds of Purpose is a series of workbooks designed to help you dig up the roots that are keeping you stagnate in the areas of:

- Rejection
- Anger
- Loss of Love
- Abandonment
- Bondage
- Jealousy/Envy
- Sexual Dysfunction

These are the core areas where people get stuck and need healing in order to grow. During your journey you will dig up the seeds that were planted by life situations, relationships, and trauma. This is not meant to replace therapy, nor is this a one-book fits all series. But for most of you it will meet you where you are and offer a path towards healing.

The workbooks can be done alone or as a group. You can

choose an accountability partner to do the process with you and then the two of you can hold each other accountable to the new journey. It is important to choose someone you trust, who will tell you the truth in love.

I am also using my story as the back drop for the healing process. I realized a few months ago that I have survived things that people have committed suicide over. I am grateful for the fortitude and grace that I have been given. But I could not have done it alone. I had God mostly and several key people walk alongside me in my healing journey, including pastors, therapists, coaches, family, and friends.

I am thankful to be able to help others do the same by sharing my story and walking alongside you. The most important thing I want you to remember is that YOU are not alone. YOU are not the only one going through this. Yes, YOU will find your way out of pain and into peace and prosperity!

Coach Athena

"If you believe you have a different root you will have different fruit." –*Creflo Dollar*

Why a Tree?

A fully bloomed, mature tree that is bearing fruit is the epitome of nature at its best. They are green, release oxygen into the atmosphere, full of life, and nature's energy. Likewise, trees that are unhealthy are not as beautiful, the color of their leaves fade, and they stop bearing fruit.

Trees gain nourishment from their roots. They have two main types of roots, structural and feeder. "The structural roots begin at the base of the tree called the root flare and keep the tree standing" (Arborilogical).[2] The feeder roots are "small fibrous roots that absorb water and minerals" (Arborilogical). [2] The roots are the foundation that keeps it standing firm, feeding the limbs, and growing, healthy, and strong. But there are times when the roots get strangled underground, usually from a foreign object that invades the soil, like concrete, waste, etc. Once the roots are damaged or poisoned, the tree begins to die. It dies slowly over time unless the roots are revived. Reviving the roots involves removing the obstruction or contamination and replanting the tree in healthy soil.

Root is defined as "something that is an origin or source (as of a condition or quality)" (Merriam-Webster).[1] The roots are a trees' source of nourishment and support. Ironically, our roots are similar. Our roots are planted in our upbringing. We are shaped through the care and nurture, or the lack of care and nurture, received in childhood. Just like the tree, our roots can get contaminated from the waste we encounter in our childhood environments, relationships, traumas, and experiences. We may also inherit the waste our parents never eliminated. There are many generations of roots living within us, some rooted so deep they choke the abundance and joy out of daily life.

How Trees Relate to Us?

Trees are symbolic because they are gender neutral. They are planted and rooted in the earth (mother). Their roots supply all they need to grow and sustain life. If a tree's roots are contaminated by the environment, the tree will stop growing, the leaves will not produce, and it will eventually die (Arborilogical). [2] The condition of the roots is crucial to sustaining life.

As humans, we are made up of mind, body, and soul which are nurtured through mental, physical, and spirit. According to Dr. Myles Munroe our spirit is gender neutral and as humans we are differentiated by our outer suit which determines gender, male or female (Munroe). [3] Similarly trees are differentiated by their suits as well, as there are different types of trees that look different but underneath function the same.

Our foundation can be likened to that of tree as well. Our structural root system is established through our upbringing, direct family life, and childhood teachings. Our feeder root system is established through our external connections in the community, at school, with friends and peers, our spiritual encounters, our food, the words we hear, and the knowledge we gain. The rate of maturity and level of maturity is dependent on these two systems working together to establish a solid foundation.

As with trees, our structural roots are created in our family life. At the beginning of life we are dependent upon our parents for everything. What they pour into us during this time and how they care for us becomes our foundation for our human structure. Parents nurture the child through feeding and caring for the infant. The important thing is to receive the proper feeding and emotional nurture from a loving caregiver (earth). As long as you are attached to your caregiver you should be growing and maturing until you reach adulthood.

Research shows that infants who "were emotionally deprived as a result of parental withdrawal, rejection, or hostility" have poor growth and do not thrive (Failure).[4] So imagine what the structural root system of a person who was abandoned as an infant/child produces. They may be unable to bond with self or others. Their physical growth may not be stopped but their emotional (mind) and spiritual (soul) roots may be immature causing them to be unbalanced and prematurely prepared for adult situations. Similarly, if a tree's structural roots are damaged because the tree was not properly nourished, when the first forceful wind whips by in a storm the tree may fall.

In their book, *The Mom Factor,* Drs. Henry Cloud and John Townsend show the relation of how nurturing received from our mothers (earth) is intended to feed us (root) spiritually and emotionally thus setting the foundation for how we relate to self and others as we grow (Cloud). [6] However, they also state that "without nurture we wither" (Cloud).[6] The failure to thrive syndrome and many other childhood problems are directly related to a lack of nurture" (Cloud). [6] In some cases, babies who were in orphanages died from lack of nurture.

As spiritual beings, your feeder roots are established from paths in your life, initially during childhood. How you relate to self and others is established from your root (childhood) experiences.

As noted earlier, if a tree's structural roots are not nourished by the earth (mother), it will not grow properly. Likewise, if your feeder roots are contaminated, it will stunt your growth as adulthood approaches. Your instincts are formed from your feeder roots and influence your inner being, guide your inner compass, and connect you spiritually to your Higher Power.

If your roots are immature and unhealthy then the spiritual connection may not be made. Proper nurturing of your roots promotes spiritual growth and maturity, creating stronger connections. Growth is stunted when the roots are choked by abandonment, rejection, loss, stress, depression, trauma, lack of love (nurturing), and negative emotions. Left untreated, you may die spiritually.

You also feed others through your fruit in relationships. Therefore, in every relationship you should strive to have healthy roots so you can produce healthy fruit. Open yourself to healing your contaminated roots during this journey.

Contaminated and Immature Roots

If you grew up without the proper nurturing you may become an adult with contaminated or immature roots. The broken connections may be seen in the patterns you repeat in your life via relationships, life choices, work, behaviors, patterns, and lifestyles. Some may even experience emotional trauma as you attempt to live a life you were not equipped for. As a result, some turn to drugs, alcohol, addictive patterns, sex, or anything that will dull the pain and allow you to cope. However, continuing to ignore the problem and not healing the roots may increase stress and the risk for physical illnesses such as high blood pressure, diabetes, heart disease, obesity, and cancer. Mental illnesses such as anxiety disorder or major depressive disorder may also result from contaminated and immature roots.

Three of my close friends died from stress related illnesses while they were too young. They were battling life issues some of which were rooted in their childhood. They did not address the root problems but continued to live and attempted to be who they were taught to be. However, in the end, they neither had the necessary foundation, nor support to keep their roots healthy and growing.

One of them was only 40 years old when she died of a massive heart attack while driving. She was not obese and she was not physically ill. She was single with no children. She still had much life to live. Her roots were contaminated and she did not handle the stress of life well. She was slowly dying emotionally and spiritually over time. But that last traumatic situation in her life was too much for her immature roots to handle.

Slow Growth

"Trees that are diseased or dying can be an eyesore, contagious, and even hazardous" (Abel). [4] A diseased tree is prone to pest infestations, limp or dry leaves, and may fall due to weak roots. However, there times when the damage is not visibly evident because the damage occurs internally. Similarly, for humans you may see the result of someone with diseased roots in their outer appearance but many are able to mask it. On the surface you look healthy but inside you are slowly dying.

10

In my own journey I lost approximately 15 years of healthy living due to contaminated roots. My growth was stunted and although I am now in my fifties, I identify with people in their thirties because I have not matured in fifteen years. Imagine what you could do in fifteen years:

✓ Earn three bachelor's degrees

✓ Buy at least three cars

✓ Pay off a mortgage

✓ Become a Medical Doctor/Lawyer

✓ Earn four master's degrees

After turning 40, I realized that I had not completed most of these things. Reality hit hard as my stagnation became obvious both emotionally and spiritually. I was overweight and diagnosed with high blood pressure, major depressive disorder, and generalized anxiety disorder because I had been living with contaminated roots and lack of nurture. This is when I began my journey of healing.

Seeds of Purpose - New Growth

This book chronicles my journey of healing and how God planted seeds of purpose to replace the contaminated roots. My process took over fifteen years because I refused to **SEE**, **ACCEPT**, and **AGREE** with my truth and my true identity. I started the process over several times before I began to see growth.

However, each person's process is different. Your journey may not take as long. It depends on your determination and ability to **SEE**, **ACCEPT**, and **AGREE** with your truth. How you respond to your truth is equally important. That's why this isn't just a book; it's a workbook with exercises and tips that you can use to facilitate your new growth.

Each workbook in the series identifies a root contamination and provides life lessons, coaching tools, and journal exercises to enable you to begin your life work now! No need to get a notebook or buy an additional workbook. You are encouraged to obtain spiritual support, an accountability partner, life coach, or therapist.

Digging up the Root

For this healing journey, you will need the following tools to be successful.

1. Strong spiritual relationship with your Higher Power
2. Commitment to be a better YOU
3. An accountability partner who will support your truth
4. A willing spirit
5. Ability to release places, people, relationships, habits, or things that stunt your growth

These tools coupled with the material presented in this book are a good starting point for your healing journey. This is not intended to be a one book heals all journey; no such book exists. But it will touch your heart and send you on a journey of healing and spiritual growth. Some of you may discover that you may need additional assistance and healing. Also, this workbook is not meant to replace any existing therapy, spiritual support, relationships, or programs. But it can be used in conjunction with them to promote wholeness.

Your healing journey will involve digging up the contaminated roots. This is done during the **SEE**, **ACCEPT**, and **AGREE** stages, where you see the spiritual root and willingly release it, accept its presence in your life, and agree that it has caused stagnation to self and others.

Now the real work begins. To truly kill contaminated roots and allow trees to grow healthy again, the entire root system must be dug up. When the tree is dug up it leaves a crater or hole in the earth. The soil in this crater is treated to make sure all contaminants are gone and then the tree is planted in healthy soil.

I am sharing the same healing process that was used to treat the soil I was planted in and to plant new seeds of purpose in my life. God will replace the old with new seed, new soil, and new growth.

Each section follows a process that is designed to help you **SEE**, **ACCEPT** and **AGREE** to your truth. You will see the following healing points throughout the book:

- **Self-Reflection:** Inspect the depths of the crater/hole.

- **Self-Work:** Dig up contaminated spirits/ways/habits that are in the hole.

- **Spiritual Work:** Kill the exposed root that causes you to do what you do.

- **Self-Discovery:** Plant new seeds by learning new ways to do things.

- **Self-Nurture:** Pour living water to begin nurturing new roots.

- **Self-Growth:** Heal the craters so new growth can begin.

Each healing point is explained in detail in the Life Lesson section of each chapter. Once you are committed to this healing journey you will begin to see new fruit blossom in your life. Do not be afraid of healing; it is refreshing, painful, and liberating.

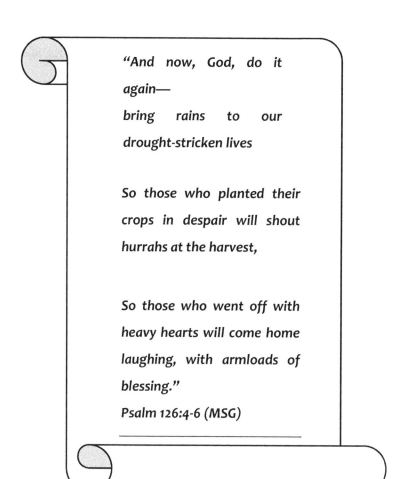

"And now, God, do it again—
bring rains to our drought-stricken lives

So those who planted their crops in despair will shout hurrahs at the harvest,

So those who went off with heavy hearts will come home laughing, with armloads of blessing."
Psalm 126:4-6 (MSG)

Seed of Anger

The state of the economy challenged many to examine their lives as they battle an enemy they cannot see whether it is a global pandemic or economic recession. Both are also things out of the immediate control of self. Many people have lost jobs they once believed would be there until retirement. Losing your life as you know it and being forced into a reality you are not prepared for does something to your perspective. Suddenly things don't look the same anymore.

A woman woke up one morning, went about her usual routine only to realize that something had changed. She no longer felt the same zest she had before perhaps it was because she was sitting at the kitchen table alone. Her youngest had started college a few weeks ago, her husband was off to his job and there she was. Alone!

A man who has invested twenty years in one company questions his next move. He was recently offered a job that he has waited his entire career for, but he's not so sure it's what he wants. He sits in his office and remembers the first day on this job. He was so excited and eager to learn everything. Now he barely makes it to work on time each morning, noticing that it takes him longer to get motivated each day. He begins to question what he would do if he did not take this job. Is there something more meaningful for him?

A son, who began working in his purpose, involuntarily abandoned his craft after a parent contracted the virus that caused the pandemic, he was mandated to quarantine for two weeks, which placed him in financial destitution. After the quarantine, his business suffered and due to his financial setbacks he had to work two unfulfilling jobs just to catch up and make ends meet, which also meant he had to temporarily step away from his purpose. Now, he wonders how he will recover from this setback and get back to the work he loves.

SELF-REVELATION

The people mentioned above have entered into some level of self-revelation as they ponder their current life choices and whether they are still meeting the same level of fulfillment in their lives. Prior to identifying your life purpose you must first know who you are and what it will take to fulfill you.

There are many ways to go about this task, but the biggest step is realizing that a change is necessary, and then taking steps to learn more about whom you are and what you are rooted in. This journey can be challenging especially if you have not spent much time with yourself. The lady in the first scenario probably hasn't spent much time with herself because as a full-time mother she has made her children her focus and was not paying close attention to self.

SELF-ISOLATION

Isolation, which may become a lonely person's best friend, is also a symptom of depression (major depressive disorder). "Social isolation can negatively affect mental health, as well as physical health. Research has found that perceived social isolation and loneliness are associated with depression, cognitive decline, poor sleep quality, a weaker immune system, and potential heart problems" (Burch).[2] In clinical psychology depression is a representation of anger turned inward. Yes, you may be angry at yourself.

"In 'Mourning and Melancholia,' which some consider Freud's

---

[2] Burch, Kelly. (2020). Social isolation negatively affects mental and physical health — here's what you can do to stay healthy. https://www.insider.com/how-social-isolation-affects-mental-health.

(1917/1957) classic paper on depression, melancholia (depression) is differentiated from mourning (grief) based on the supposition that in melancholia, anger is directed toward the self in the form of self-reproach and self-attack, in contrast to mourning, where anger is directed toward the lost love object" (Lamia).[3] Loneliness is an emotion that may produce thoughts of self-isolation and self-pity because you may believe that you are disliked by everyone. All of us experience some level of loneliness. But for some there are self-inflicted bouts of loneliness which is called self-isolation. These bouts are not usually positive they become "pity parties" where we sit with our self and berated self because of past traumas, pain, or mistakes.

We have recently experienced mandated bouts of loneliness through mandatory quarantines. This mandate has placed many into emotional positions they are not ready to face. The "pity party" is forced and ongoing, either situation whether self-inflicted or mandated, may lead to a buildup of emotions with no outlet.

---

[3] Source: Lamia, Mary C. (2019). The Perplexing Notion of Depression as "Anger Turned Inward": An attack-self coping response to shame is prominent in depression. https://www.psychologytoday.com/us/blog/intense-emotions-and-strong-feelings/201906/the-perplexing-notion-depression-anger-turned.

The extended bouts of loneliness may increase the anger at self which may lead to depression.

SELF-ANGER

Self-anger is exhibited in different ways depending upon the person, situation, and emotional state. My self-anger exhibited in my relationships. I closed myself off from people and placed myself in situations that could have harmed me and others. I never desired to take my life. I didn't do deliberate acts to physically hurt self or others. But these are ways that self-anger may exhibit in others.

God's glory is always with me. I am thankful that I am able to help others identify and dig up their roots of anger through my journey. In my journey, living with loneliness for many years or the majority of my life lead to deeper feelings of sadness and worthlessness that lead to deep self-resentment and major depressive disorder.

HOW THE SEED WAS WATERED

The seed of anger was introduced during my childhood. I was shy, quiet, and often overlooked. I had what I call, middle child syndrome, if that really exists. I was a middle child but wasn't the baby for long and I wasn't the first. Most of the attention went to the first and the last. Therefore, I don't recall being regarded as someone's special one. So, growing up I felt as if I existed in my world alone, like I didn't fit in.

I wasn't popular in school either. I didn't have many friends in elementary school mainly because we moved so much. But during middle school and high school I did have a few friends, but I wasn't popular or a social butterfly. I was often referred to as my brother's sister because he was the popular one. I just didn't fit in so I didn't try. That motivated me to stay to myself even more.

My early childhood memories are full of family moments that are endearing, fun, and exciting. We used to go to the beach on the weekends. We would get up at dawn to the smell of fried chicken. Mama would tell us to hurry and get ready. I was excited because I was going to swim. I love the water! It is so peaceful.

These family outings were the highlight of my childhood. My aunt lived next door. So we would all go to the beach together along with their other friend and her children. We would get out there early in the morning and stay all day until sundown.

Mama was happy then and so was I. But I still spent a lot of time alone. When we were at the beach, I usually played alone or swam alone. I very seldom played with my siblings, or my cousins. When we were inside, my brother and I played together, but when our cousins came around, they went off on their own. And that was fine because even at six years old, I was an introvert.

Life changed once mama got married. I was nine when our fun times at the beach and other family gatherings went away. My step father is a military veteran and also did not have any children when he married mama. Everyone's life changed dramatically. Overnight he inherited a full family with four kids and we suddenly had a daddy in the house.

Life transitions can be the most emotionally charged times in life. If not handled well, they may become traumatic which create triggers. Traumatic transitions are not always negative; they can be points of growth as well. My transition was traumatic because I felt like I lost my mama. Not literally but mama was not available like before and she struggled to find balance. During those years I remember the adults saying, "Children are to be seen and not heard", out of respect. The adults also did not discuss adult situations with children, not even to explain that life is changing. We often repeat the patterns of our parents. Their parents did not communicate these life transitions to them either. Culturally we have left our children in the dark. When this happens it leaves the child's mind to develop their own explanation about why these things are happening.

In my journey, I related everything to rejection which fed my self-anger. These were based on the perceptions of a lonely little girl. I stopped talking deliberately when I was constantly teased and not allowed to speak without interruption. These became patterns and triggers for my anger. I would not directly address the anger, trauma, or person. I learned to be invisible and as I got older I retreated into isolation, self-hate, and fear which became the brew that birthed the seed of anger from my loneliness.

This dysfunction planted a seed of anger and as my roots grew, it left a gaping hole. I developed a passive aggressive pattern similar to what was displayed in my childhood. There was anger, angry words, and unhealthy responses to angry outbursts. My childhood coping mechanism spilled over into adulthood. I had friends and love interests who triggered me when they displayed a pattern similar to a childhood trauma or said something to dig up a traumatic transition.

In my cycle I would simply cut people out of my life instead of trying to resolve the issue and preserve the relationship. I did this as a form of self-protection believing if I did not allow people to get close, they would not leave or reject me. I wasn't aware then, but I'd been attracting people who carried similar passive aggressive spirits or demeanor. This caused me to feel even more alone in my intimate relationships with men specifically, affecting my ability to trust and love.

RELATIONSHIPS

I got married when I was 25 years old. I committed myself to making my marriage work especially after we had our children.

This is when most of my roots began to resurface. I let my guard down and allowed myself to be vulnerable. But there was a lot of contention between us. I used to say we were like oil and water. But seriously we both brought our emotional baggage into our marriage. I discovered how deeply my pain went during this relationship. I did not like the woman I had become and it hit me hard. It brought a new type of loneliness into my already lonely existence. This is part of what I discovered about how my roots attributed to how I related to men. I wanted intimacy but was afraid of it at the same time. I would only allow a man to know the woman with the mask. When someone tried to remove the mask I would respond defensively and become verbally combative. "But each battle only damaged my roots even more.

> I am scared of intimacy but afraid of being alone. Just as I did, as a child, I adjusted to being alone. The isolation got worse as our fights worsened. I had to prepare myself for the isolation. This was a new level of loneliness. We didn't communicate well especially our emotions. Toward the end [of our

27

relationship] we didn't even sleep together.[4]

Intimacy was not something I gravitated to, but at the time I didn't realize how intertwined all of my issues were. The seed of rejection fed the seed of loneliness; the seed of loneliness grew into a seed of anger. The seed of anger was watered by low self-esteem because I believed that people were purposely rejecting me. The negative self-talk produced by the anger tortured me for most of my twenties and also fed my depression. As I became more depressed, I felt more worthless. As a worthless, angry woman with low self-esteem, the negative self-talk watered my seed of sexual dysfunction, which caused me to seek sex instead of intimacy. My inability to be intimate with God and self-first, then with others triggered my spiral into major depressive disorder.

---

[4] Thomas, Athena. Journal Entry. 2001

> *"Today I was feeling alone; ready to plunge into another depression. I called out to my Father.*
>
> *While I was working and listening to my music I realized how lonely I am. There is so much distance in this house. I don't know why it surprises me sometimes, but it does."[5]*

Our initial intimate relationship is experienced with our mother. We are intimately connected to her in the womb. When we are born we establish the intimate bond with our father as well. This intimacy grows throughout our childhood, becoming our foundation for relationships. [6]

Instead of creating intimate bonds, I created dysfunctional relationships. My inability to connect intimately with my parents played out in my relationship with my ex-husband and fed the depression. I unconsciously attracted men who also could not connect intimately, who struggled with addiction, were verbally insulting, and passive aggressive.

---

[5] Thomas, Athena. Journal Entry. 2001

As a result of this and other dysfunctional relationships with men, I became afraid to be alone. It was now more attractive to be with him and miserable than to be alone. During counseling I discovered that I was being codependent.

"Codependency involves sacrificing one's personal needs to try to meet the needs of others."[6] The definition the describes how the root evolved into codependency states it as "sharing the responsibility for the unhealthy behavior, primarily by focusing their lives on the sick or the bad behavior and by making their own self-esteem and well-being contingent on the behavior of the unhealthy family member."[7] I became overly consumed with his problems which became my excuse for not focusing on self. This was also a repetitious pattern from my childhood as I watched my mother do the same. I watched her needs and desires shrink more and more as she sought to keep things intact at home for us.

---

[6] *Codependency*. GoodTherapy. 2020.
https://www.goodtherapy.org/learn-about-therapy/issues/codependency
[7] DuPont and McGovern, p. 316

FRIENDSHIPS

I was the oldest girl and did not have a sisterhood friendship before my teen years. So, I yearned to have a sisterly bond with a friend. My sisters are much younger than I and by the time they were old enough to have a sisterly relationship, I was grown and married. I attended a friend's event and she asked her sisters to stand. I stood because we have a sisterly bond. I didn't realize at the time she was also referring to her "line sisters." I was not a "line sister" and never would be. They experienced some things together that bonded them for life and I would never be a part of that. But the experience helped me reexamine what sisterhood really is.

As a teenager I had one close girlfriend. I never had a group of girlfriends. Being an introvert, I did not purposely draw attention to myself to make friends. That trend continued when I became an adult. At worksites, I would stay to myself. I was quiet and did not engage others unless it related to work. Over the course of the years I did make a few friends at work. But I found that most of the relationships did not survive past the workplace.

But even my relationships with the friends I did have were limited. I still spent quite a bit of my time alone or feeling lonely and was unable to express it to anyone. I didn't feel worthy of true friendship and I never felt that they genuinely wanted to be my friend. It always felt as if they were around to get something from me. These beliefs stemmed from the negative self-talk. Even though this happened only once or twice, it became my reality for every friendship; I just didn't believe they were sincere so I shut myself off from accepting true friendship and love.

Examples of my negative self-talk:

> *"No one on this earth really has friends. You think someone is your friend but they're really not. You think you can trust someone or be trusted by someone who calls themselves your friend but you can't."*

> *"Once again I find myself all alone. Well I am not totally alone because I always have You (speaking to God). I have been going through this for years now. People (friends) come into my life and we get attached, close and then something happens that separates us. Two have left in the last two months. It hurts to see how they are treating me as a result."*[8]

---

[8] *Thomas, Athena. Journal Entry. 2020*

I looked to my peers to establish that sisterhood. I had one friend whom I considered a sister. We were bonded in two ways by family and then by circumstances. We did go through some things together. She was there through my marriage, major life losses, depression, death, financial ruin, and birth of my children. I also walked through many of her lowest moments by her side. We kept each other's secrets and I vowed to always be her sister, because she didn't have one. However this relationship ended unfavorably as well, several times.

EXPOSED ROOTS

I keep dreaming about houses. In the last dream I was in a struggle. I was running from something. I have visualized most of my friends in some form spiritually. It makes me question myself. Have I ever hurt someone this way because of my own internal pain?[9]

According to dream psychology a house represents "self" the soul, thoughts, feelings of self. In this particular dream I was in a struggle inside the house. So if the house represents self then I was in a struggle with myself. I realized that most of my struggles with self are about external issues I am avoiding in my life. That internal fight fuels the anxious thoughts that keep me in my anger cycle too long. So the dreams serve as a tool to help me focus on the specific issue in my waking life-outside of the cycle-to initiate healing in that area.

In the journal entry above I acknowledge my battle with self. During my spiritual healing journey, I learned to always look in my mirror before attempting to place blame on others. So my

---

[9] Thomas, Athena. Journal Entry. 2020

question to self is "*Have I ever hurt someone this way because of my own internal pain?*" My soul work revealed that I never hated anyone but I did hurt several people with my words or actions. Out of fear I would shut down and end relationships abruptly. More evidence of how my exposed roots affected how I related to self and friends.

My cycle of contention starts with anxiety which is not always based on actual fear but conceived fear of a particular situation. One of my triggers is betrayal with my man. Yes, I have had more than one girlfriend cross that line. One time my reaction was not the best and I said some things out of anger that hurt her and damaged our relationship. That lesson taught me to be slower to speak especially after I understood the source of the anger. I was reacting from a place of old hurt unconsciously. I believe the saying that "Hurt people hurt people." Once my spiritual eyes were open, could SEE the pattern and take steps to change it. Now I vent the anger in a healthy way, then attempt to have the conversation when there is a disagreement with a friend.

CHALLENGES

Each of the friends presented in my dreams represented a part of me that I was struggling with. I realized that part of my struggle was about forgiving me for poor choices that hurt me and others. It is a struggle to face the dark parts of self, the parts we don't like or want others to SEE. But they exist and usually are some type of defense mechanism we put in place to protect ourselves emotionally.

I also struggled with how others would perceive me as I told my truth. People are less forgiving than you think. While it may seem easy for me to bare these intimate things about self in this book, it stills comes with a bit of anxiety. But as I have adopted a growth mindset in my life, I now realize that we can change any aspect of being when we are committed to it and allow ourselves to believe that change is possible. A fixed mindset tells you that you will never change and will always continue to struggle. Therefore we avoid the struggle-hence no growth. But guess what, we are human and we all make mistakes that turn into challenges to be better.

"In a growth mindset, challenges are exciting rather than threatening. So rather than thinking, oh, I'm going to revel my weaknesses, you say, wow, here's a chance to grow." -- Carol S. Dweck, Ph.D., Author of Mindset The New Psychology of Success

Killing the Root

The Spirit Himself bears witness with our spirit that we are children of God, [17]and if children, then heirs--heirs of God and joint heirs with Christ, if indeed we suffer with Him, that we may also be glorified together. (Romans 8:16-17)

Now, therefore, you are no longer strangers and foreigners, but fellow citizens with the saints and members of the household of God, [20]having been built on the foundation of the apostles and prophets, Jesus Christ Himself being the chief cornerstone, [21]in whom the whole building, being fitted together, grows into a holy temple in the Lord, [22]in whom you also are being built together for a dwelling place of God in the Spirit. (Ephesians 2:19)

Hebrews 13:5 says, "Let your conduct be without covetousness; be content with such things as you have. For He

Himself has said, 'I will never leave you nor forsake you.'" And he hasn't. Although people have left me or I have felt alone, there were many times when God was the only one I could turn to and I am thankful that He was there.

Contentment

What does it mean to be content? Contentment is defined as a state of peaceful happiness. Contentment is passive; satisfaction is active. The former is the mindset of one who does not needlessly pine after what is beyond his reach, nor fret at the hardship of his condition. The latter is the mindset of one who has all he desires and feels pleasure in the contemplation of his situation. Allowing yourself to be content in your current state is a form of acceptance. It's like taking inventory. You may not have reached the goal yet, but your daily work towards it shows progress which equals current contentment. You are satisfied that you are making progress towards the goal.

A deprived person may be content, but can hardly be satisfied. How is a deprived person content but not satisfied? Our perceptions or faulty roots influence our level of satisfaction and feeds our anger, which if untreated can lead to further despair and giving up on life. A deprived person is someone lacking the appropriate life nutrients to be whole and live a healthy life. The lack of life nutrients may be due to unresolved childhood trauma, recent trauma, life mistakes, anxiety, life choices, mental illness, physical illness, emotional trauma, abuse, etc. Our negative life experiences feed us just as much as the positive life experiences. Only they don't promote growth, they promote stagnation.

Deprived Trees

Did you know you can plant a tree, decide not to feed it the right nutrients, and it will still grow to maturation? It takes trees decades to mature, but during that time, its growth will produce fragile leaves, poor nutrients, immature or sick fruit etc. Growth continues even if the roots are damaged.

Signs of a dying or sick oak tree are seen in its outward appearance. The top branches may be dead or broken off, the bark is yellow or brown, and there is fungus growth or insect and animal habitation.[10] We continue to grow as well despite what we are fed spiritually, emotionally, and psychologically. What are the signs of a deprived person who is slowing dying or has given up on life?

According to a study by John Leach, "the term 'give-up-it is' describes people who respond to traumatic stress by developing extreme apathy, give up hope, relinquish the will to live, and die, despite no obvious organic cause."[11] The condition occurs in five stages:[12]

1. Social Withdrawal – exhibited by "lack of emotion, listlessness (a coping mechanisms to attempt to pull back from outward emotional engagement as a means to realign emotion stability"[9]

2. Apathy – "a deep sense of melancholy that can indicate a person no longer strive for self-preservation"[9]

---

[10] Timber Works Tree Care. Signs Your Oak Tree is Dying. 7/14/2020. Retrieved from https://timberworksva.com/signs-your-oak-tree-is-dying/

[11] Leach, J. Give-up-itis' revisited: Neuropathology of extremis. Medical Hypotheses. Volume 120. 2018. Pages 14-21. ISSN 0306-9877. https://doi.org/10.1016/j.mehy.2018.08.009. (http://www.sciencedirect.com/science/article/pii/S0306987718306145)

[12] Purdy, Chase. 2018. Giving up on life can lead to actual death in less than a month. https://qz.com/1407287/giving-up-on-life-can-lead-to-actual-death-in-less-than-a-month/

3. Aboulia – "physical activity starts to drop off and the brain switches to standby mode which causes loss of motivation"[9]

4. Psychic akinesia – being apathetic towards pain which results in the persons lack of motivation to remove self from danger[9]

5. Psychogenic death – Disintegration of a person, the actual point of giving up[9]

How Do I Stop Hurting Self

2020 flooded the spotlight on loopholes, flaws, truth, and fears, in us, our country, and our way of life, which resulted in unhealthy angry outburst in homes, in cities and neighborhoods, and in and towards our government. Millions watched the unhealthy release of anger in riots and protests as people walked in fear of an invisible enemy.

You can learn how to heal by examining the actions and responses of self and others during a crisis. Healing involves releasing the old to make room for the new. The Bible states that it is not wise to put new wine in old wineskins. It will distort the freshness, pureness, and taste of the wine. So before you can walk in your new path, spirit, vibrations, and revelations, you need to release your anger in a healthy way.

Dig Up Roots

In order to dig up your childhood roots you have to first be able to see them as they are. This is done during the SEE stage where you allow yourself to connect spiritually. Everyone has a different process for how they connect spiritually.

44

In my process I use prayer, meditation, and music. I allow the music to lift my spirit and prepare me to have a conversation God. Then I make my petition or set my intention. My intentions were:

1. To SEE the specific roots that was keeping me from growing.

2. To SEE how those roots contribute to my contentious cycle.

3. To SEE how my actions contribute to my contentious cycle.

During my spiritual process God exposed five roots and how they hindered my growth.

- Self-identity

- Abandonment

- Repetition of pattern

- Rejection

- Lack of Protection

I will use one root to describe how God dug up the exposed root. There is an exercise in the Self-Nurture section where you can complete this process for your exposed roots.

SEE - Lack of protection

The SEE stage exposed the root of lack of protection. It originated in my childhood and how I received both maternal and paternal influences. The maternal influence was the seed of contention and the paternal influence was the seed of lack of protection.

I remember my father living with us until I was about four or five years old. My parents' divorced and my mom remarried when I was nine years old. I was raised by my mom, my stepfather, and my grandmother. During these years there was contention in the house. God showed that this is where the seed of contention was planted.

When my parents' divorced I also lost the protective covering of my father. Although I still had a father figure in the home, the absence of my father produced a root and many years of daddy issues when I became a woman. The combination of these roots produced anxiety and fear, especially when I was vulnerable. When I was in a vulnerable state I would experience racing thoughts, mostly negative, I would talk myself out of doings things that would allow me to be emotionally close to people.

After experiencing several traumatic life experiences, many by my poor choices, the anxiety became worse and began to exhibit as anger. The anger became my mask for fear. So when I was hurt emotionally, instead of crying, I would get angry. But when the hurt cut me deeper, I would exhibit both anger and tears. I learned in therapy that at this point, I was shut down emotionally.

The lack of foundation on both sides produced a crater full of pain, betrayal, self-anger, and low self-esteem that manifested in all of my relationships. It's important to note that neither of my parents knew this was happening to me. I first became aware in my late thirties when depression almost took my life.

This was confirmed when I watched it happened to my own children when my marriage ended. There was no way to prevent the planting of that seed because all of sudden their father was gone and they lost the covering of their father. I internalized this as well, because I was the one who left the marriage. But I did not do it hastily. It was a choice between life and death. Although I chose life, it also killed some things for all of us.

Realizing that my children were now reliving my childhood, I decided to heal our family though mental health counseling. All of us worked in family counseling to address the seeds planted during the divorce. Getting my children help early helped them to process the seeds that were planted so that they did not grow into unhealthy roots of anger.

ACCEPT – Lack of Protection

During the ACCEPT stage God told me it was not my fault. As a little girl I internalized everything and blamed myself for my father and grandmother not being in my life, in believed there was something wrong with me. My message from God said it was not my fault because as children we internalize things that happen to us. How many kids have you seen who believe that when their parents split up it was something they did? Well I believed that as well. The negative self-talk from the anxiety watered that seed for years. But finally last year, I accepted the truth that it was not fault.

How I Contributed

I do not consider myself to be a victim-although things were done to me unwillingly-I chose many of the paths I ended up on. When those paths turned into trauma and chaos, I again internalized the pain and blamed myself. This manifested many ways in my relationships, especially with men.

I never trusted a man to protect me after losing my father. I attempted to open up to my first love, but lack of commitment made me put the mask back on. I also discovered that this was my first manifestation of those roots in my adult relationships. The seeds were watered more by my response. I made a choice not to trust my heart to a man again and chose to have uncommitted relationships. This was another mask and form of self-protection.

AGREE – Lack of Protection

In the AGREE stage God told me that I have to forgive. I had to forgive my parents because they didn't do anything to me deliberately. They were young and were probably repeating what they saw as well. But most importantly I have to forgive myself.

Understanding that life is a cycle will help you develop the ability to forgive. During my process God showed me my parents struggle as young adults, young parents, and with their own roots. They did not know that their actions or decisions were hurting me. God also showed me that there was a legacy of patterns and generational curses in my family. We repeat what we SEE.

Forgiveness helps you heal. Even if the event that you were shown was done deliberately to you forgiveness will help you begin the healing process. Forgive your parents or the person who was revealed to you in the SEE stage.

All of these seeds were rooted somewhere in my childhood watered by my life choices and experiences. During our family counseling I learned how my exposed roots were planting damaging seeds for my children as well. This laid a foundation for healing and started the process to fill the crater with new seeds of purpose.

No one comes out of childhood without some emotional scars but when you mix trauma and contention it can be a deadly cocktail for deep rooted emotional pain. You must acknowledge that you were hurt or disappointed and then make a decision not to live in that pain anymore. Then find a path to refilling that hole with something healthy, purposeful, and positive. This is a crucial step in your healing journey. If the roots are not dug up and replaced with good seeds they will resurface.

Have you ever seen a tree's roots protruding through the dirt? If they are left this way the elements may damage the roots and the tree may die. As stated earlier a sick tree needs to be replanted in good soil deep enough so the roots have room to expand and allowing the tree to survive and thrive.

Nevertheless I Live

Heated
Anger
Towards
Ego (Self)

Your anger is not
For me
You abhor my achievements
While you haven't attempted

Nevertheless I live

You despise
My wings because they
Carry me
Despite the secretly plucked feathers

Nevertheless I live

You are repelled by
My beauty
My quiet inner self
I am intrigued although you steal
Right in my face

Nevertheless I live

You denounce the mirror reflection
Of my heart
His willful profession, protection, provision

Nevertheless I live

You loathe
My life

Nevertheless I live

Despite your physical torture
I Laugh
Despite your emotional turmoil
I Love
Despite your stabs in my heart

Nevertheless I Live

Life Lesson - Seed of Anger

"... The contentions of a wife are like a continual dripping [of water through a chink in the roof]." Proverbs 19:13

Loneliness engulfed my daily life to the point where I was unconsciously walking in self-anger. Especially when I realized that I chose each person who was in my life. I chose my words, my behavior, and my path. I maintained certain relationships even when I saw that they were not bringing anything good to my life. God showed me that I was a key player in the chaos that existed in my relationships, as a result of my contentious cycle, especially in my marriage. I unconsciously repeated this cycle over and over in every relationship.

Now it is your turn to identify your contentious cycle. This is the first step in digging up those roots of anger. You have to SEE what you are contributing to the Universe through your cycle.

Directions: In this lesson you will take time to examine your behavior and find your contentious cycle.

The Contentious Cycle

When engulfed in loneliness, you are not always eager to look at self in a critical way. Our inner eyes tend to focus on what we do are lacking which produces the feelings of loneliness.

If you are continuing our journey, you may have spent time looking at yourself and where you are right now. As a result you may have discovered some things that were unpleasant. In fact, we all have a disagreeable side and it is that part of us that God wants to clean up and make white as snow. Now it is time to look at your inner mirror and identify your contentious cycle.

This scripture quoted above clearly depicts the impact of

contentions on the spouse. To help you understand this better, first I want to give you some background on the scripture and what it means.

First let's define some words. **Contentious** means *"given to contention; quarrelsome"* and **contentions** means, *"The act or an instance of striving in controversy or debate; an assertion put forward in argument; a dispute where there is strong disagreement."* **Brawling** is defined as, *"disposed to loud disagreements and fighting."*

Next, women are not the only ones who have a contentious cycle. A person with a contentious cycle is always fussing, arguing, and fighting with their spouse, their kids, their family, and their friends. They are never content. Nothing you do will satisfy them. They are always ready for a fight and to put someone in their place when they look like they are about or do cross you.

A contentious person is also one who fights their own battles. You will never allow anyone to fight on your behalf, especially not her man, if it is a woman. But often your spouse is the target of your contentions. If your spouse is the target you may notice that he/she finds ways to get away from you or to conveniently be away from home. You may begin to think that this is because your spouse is creeping. Why would the person who has confessed their love to you not want to be around you? Why do your children avoid you and do not want to invite their friends over?

Matthew Henry's Commentary says it best.

> *"What a great affliction it is to a man to have a brawling, scolding woman as a wife. Who upon every occasion and often upon no occasion breaks out into a passion, and chides either him or those about her, is fretful to herself and furious to her children and servants, and in both vexatious to her husband."*

Vexatious means *"to annoy and cause distress."* It is quite disturbing to know that I may have caused someone distress to this extreme. In an attempt to escape the distress the man tries to find the best way to deal with it. Now if it is a worldly man the results could be quite disastrous because he will fight with worldly weapons, which mean that he may become aggressive, passive-aggressive, spew angry words at others, or self-medicate with alcohol, drugs, or sex. It can manifest in many ways. The important thing is to remember that it is not about you nor did you directly cause them to respond that way. Unresolved life issues like these will come up again in relationships and patterns. Thus begins a spiral into the pits of chaos for both.

But a spiritual person should respond in a different way. According to Matthew Henry's Commentary:

> *"He finds it his best way to retire into a corner of the house top and sit alone there, out of the hearing of her clamor; and if he employ himself well there, as he may do it is the wisest course he can take. Better do so than quit the house, and go into bad company, for diversion, as many, who like Adam, make their wife's sin the excuse of their own."*

I am not saying that the reasons why some spouses are aggressive is the fault of the contentious partner but sometimes the contentious behavior acts as a trigger and takes you back into that painful moment like it just happened. When this occurs your mind kicks into flight or fight mode because a possible threat has been revealed. Your automatic defense walls come up along with those worldly spirits, emotions, or responses. Most aggressive people were already this way before they entered your life because they do not have adequate coping skills and are living in their contentious cycle themselves.

But the focus of this lesson is on you. Are you a contentious person? Use the following exercise to help determine the answer to this question.

Exercise 1 (SEE)

The purpose of this exercise is to define your contentious cycle. Write about your last argument and answer the following questions. Be honest with yourself. You will not overcome this if you are not honest. Complete this exercise after each argument or disagreement with your spouse, friends, etc., and you will begin to see a cycle.

- What was the argument about?

_____

_____

_____

_____

_____

_____

_____

_____

_____

_____

_____

_____

_____

- Who was it with?

_____

_____

_____

_____

_____

_____

_____

_____

_____

_____

- Who started it?

_____

_____

_____

_____

_____

_____

_____

_____

_____

_____

- Who ended it?

_____

_____

_____

_____

_____

_____

_____

_____

_____

_____

- What was the resolution?

_____

_____

_____

_____

_____

_____

_____

_____

_____

_____

_____

_____

- How did you feel after the argument?_____

_____

_____

_____

_____

_____

_____

_____

_____

_____

_____

_____

_____

_____

_____

_____

_____

_____

_____

_____

_____

_____

_____

Exercise 2 (ACCEPT) – Identify your cycle.

When I completed this exercise, I was surprised about what was revealed in my cycle because although I blamed self internally. Externally I pointed fingers outwardly in my relationships.

My Contentious Cycle

My ex-husband and I argued a lot. Looking back now I realize that I initiated many of those arguments. The most common ones stemmed from a request. It could have been something as small as going to the store to buy me a soda and him bringing back the wrong soda. Upon his return with the wrong item I would begin an argument about how he didn't love me because he didn't know what I liked. I felt that he should have known what I liked and what I didn't like without me having to keep telling him. I would end up verbally belittling him, fussing until no end, and most of the time the argument would not end until I said so. He would try to walk away from me but I would follow him through the house until I was finished. Nothing ever got resolved during these arguments and each one left me feeling even emptier.

This pattern was similar to how I treated myself in those self-anger moments. When I was in my pity party I would belittle self, blame self, and not let up until I was depressed. I could not have acknowledged this when I was in the relationship because I did not SEE it. But I still expected my ex-husband to magically know what I desired. I expected him to make me feel better about myself and when it did not happen that would trigger my contentious cycle.

My journey out of this cycle started when God told me to focus on self and stop looking at others. With the help of several psychological and spiritual counselors I was able to look in my inner mirror and ACCEPT what I saw. The accept stage can be challenging and may require an accountability partner or professional to help you successfully complete it. Once I was able to SEE it and ACCEPT it I became consciously aware of my pattern and my responses. Therefore when I found myself in a similar situation I was able to apply what I learned during counseling to break the cycle.

Transformation takes time and there will be plenty of

opportunities presented to practice the new cycle and responses when you AGREE to God's new path.

> *"It is better to shun bitter contention by pouring out the heart before God. For prudence and patience, with constant prayer, the cross may be removed."* (Matthew *Henry's Commentary Concise)*

Use the journal space below to identify the cycle that was revealed in exercise one. This will become your first look at your cycle. Write about the revelations, the emotions that came up, and what was confirmed. Identify what you need assistance with changing.

_____

_____

_____

_____

_____

_____

_____

_____

_____

_____

_____

_____

_____

_____

_____

_____

_____

_____

_____

_____

_____

_____

_____

_____

_____

_____

_____

_____

_____

_____

_____

_____

_____

_____

_____

_____

_____

_____

_____

_____

_____

_____

_____

_____

_____

_____

_____

_____

_____

What Are You Rooted In? Planting Seeds of Purpose for Anger

_____

_____

_____

_____

_____

_____

_____

_____

_____

_____

_____

_____

_____

_____

_____

_____

_____

_____

_____

_____

_____

_____

_____

_____

_____

_____

_____

_____

_____

_____

_____

_____

_____

_____

_____

_____

_____

_____

Exercise 3 (AGREE) – Spiritual Work

Pray or meditate on these intentions:

Thank you for allowing me to SEE myself through Your spiritual mirror. Thank you for showing me my truth and allowing me to ACCEPT what I saw. I pray for the spiritual guidance needed to begin this new journey. Help me start the work necessary to address what was revealed in the beginning of this journey. Help me understand how I landed at this point.

Show me the root associated with the emotions, patterns, and roots that surfaced. Help me identify areas where I may need professional support or an accountability partner and give me the strength to ask for help with my healing and acceptance.

Cover me in Your full armor, encase me in Your protective angel bubble, show me the spiritual, psychological, and emotional wellness tools needed to succeed on this journey. Open my third eye to SEE my path to peace and prosperity.

Seeds of Purpose

Write about what is revealed spiritually after the prayer or meditation. These are your seeds of purpose. What is new? What do you need to work on? What are your next steps?

_____

_____

_____

_____

_____

_____

_____

_____

_____

_____

_____

_____

_____

_____

_____

_____

_____

_____

_____

_____

_____

_____

_____

_____

_____

_____

_____

_____

_____

_____

_____

_____

_____

_____

_____

_____

_____

_____

_____

_____

_____

_____

_____

_____

_____

_____

_____

_____

_____

_____

_____

_____

_____

_____

_____

_____

_____

_____

_____

_____

_____

_____

_____

_____

_____

_____

_____

_____

_____

_____

_____

_____

_____

_____

_____

_____

_____

_____

_____

_____

_____

_____

_____

_____

_____

_____

_____

_____

_____

_____

_____

_____

_____

_____

_____

_____

Self-Nurture

Now it is time to nurture your roots and seal the crater with good positive affirmations about self. The process planting new seeds takes time. Give yourself the necessary time to heal and grow. Everyone's path to healing is different so do not use others to measure your growth. Instead keep a spiritual journal and keep track of what you discover. When you go back and review it each month, you will begin to SEE a positive change in your cycle and life.

Use the exercise below to start and maintain your spiritual healing journey.

Exercise:

1. If you have an active prayer life, prepare yourself in your usual way. In the prayer ask that your spiritual eyes are opened, so that you can SEE your growth.

2. If you meditate prepare yourself as you normally would for meditative state of peace and truth. Ask that your spiritual guides help you see your roots and growth in this area.

3. If you use music to prepare your spirit. Enter into a mode of worship and state your intentions to the Spirit to SEE your growth.

These are only a few suggestions for preparing self to receive spiritual guidance. Culturally you may have another process. It is important to use what will help you achieve a safe space to allow self to open and receive what God has to show you.

Congratulations, you have just completed your second step in healing on your path to peace and prosperity. Now it is time to nurture and celebrate YOU.

Treat yourself:

- to a nice spiritual bath or shower,
- on a date to your favorite restaurant, or
- a vacation for one (not frivolous),

But purposely give yourself a treat that will make you feel special and loved.

 *Self-Growth*

When you begin a new journey, it is hard to know what to do especially when you are in uncharted waters. Your self-growth activity is geared towards helping you chart a new course based upon what you have learned about yourself on this journey.

> *"People who do not release their self-anger will not become hugely successful because they are unavailable." –Bishop T.D. Jakes*

Create a chart of the exposed roots and what key things were revealed during each stage. Use the chart as a visual guide for healing or expand it to chart your progress.

EXPOSED ROOT	SEE	ACCEPT	AGREE
Self-Identity	How your inner child was shaped by: Maternal: Paternal: Siblings:	I did not SEE the six year old self was buried In the roots of my parents' divorce; as a result the girl did not grow internally.	Agree to change my lens. Stop focusing on "others" and look at me until I understand who I am and how I fit into God's plan. Discover my life purpose and measure how off course I am as a result of the exposed roots. Discover how to live with fewer setbacks

EXPOSED ROOT	SEE	ACCEPT	AGREE

Setting Goals

Setting goals is a way to establish an action plan to initiate a new life path. Set a goal for one new item, purpose, goal, or challenge, revealed in your work, which requires change. Next, use the questions to develop an action plan to overcome it.

Use the Goal Planning Template and worksheet with your accountability partner to start your action plan to break your contentious cycle and walk in your new path. Remember that your goal should be **SMART** = **S**pecific, **M**easurable, **A**chievable, **R**ealistic, and **T**ime Bound.

Goal Planning Template

Information			
Name:			
Life Project:			
Coach/Accountability Partner:			
Main Value:		Review Period:	**to**
Instructions			

Goals should be: **S** – Specific **M** – Measurable **A** – Achievable **R** – Realistic **T** – Time Bound

1. **Goal/Objective**. Briefly describe each goal/objective and when the goal/objective should be met or accomplished. Include the value or anti-value that is associated with this goal.
2. **Measurement**. How will the goal/objective be evaluated? (Use quantitative measures such as % or dollar increases in revenue or market share and/or use qualitative measures which are descriptive of criteria.)
3. **Importance**. Rank the goal as Essential, Important, or Desirable as follows:

Essential – required for personal success   **Long Term Goal** - 6 to 9 Months

Important – helpful for personal success   **Performance Goal** - 1 to 3 months

Desirable – asset for personal success   **Meeting Goal** - Daily

Growth Steps: Apply the growth steps to each of your goals. Use what you have learned to identify as many known hurdles, roadblocks, and barriers that you may encounter on your journey.

Jump Into New Things/Hurdles - Represents those things that keep you from jumping into new things. What are you afraid of? What keeps you from starting your journey?

Work Around Unforeseen Roadblocks - Represents unforeseen things that block your progress on your path to purpose. May be an unexpected illness, trauma, or hardship.

Life Adjustments/Barriers - Represents things that cannot be moved but may require life adjustments. For example, becoming a parent for the first time may present some barriers but not stop you from progressing with a few life adjustments.

Sample Goal Sheet w/answers

1st Goal/Objective

Description: *Be early, productive and proactive.*

Values: Joy – *make me happy* Integrity – *person of word* ;**Trust** – *trust others will do what they say*; **Groundedness** – *not sporadic you know what you are doing.*
Anti-values: Laziness (sometimes I procrastinate) **Conflict** (lateness causes conflict) **Stress** (lateness contributes to stress)

Measurement: *Every time I have a commitment I will write it down. Continue to journal about meetings/commitments on the calendar. Review notes once per week. Compare them to see progress or points for improvement.*

Importance: ☐ ***Essential***   ☐ Important   ☐ Desirable

Type: ☐ Long Term Goal   ☐ ***Performance Goal***   ☐ Meeting Goal

Desired Goal Completion Date: October 31, 3019

Growth Steps: Identify possible hurdles, roadblocks, or barriers that may hinder your progress on this goal and how you plan to overcome them.

Everything is new about this process because I have never been on time.

How will you jump over hurdles? *Your wardrobe choice in advance. I put on everything before I leave the house.*

Five seconds, the more I prep I won't' go. Have five seconds to get out of the car. Walk in with positive thoughts.

Identify when it's just a conversation or a commitment. Take time to clarify. Being productive is overwhelming – need assistance.

How will you work around roadblocks? *Give myself more time to get ready. Give myself a buffer of extra time to get there.*

(Productivity and proactive) Set the right expectations. Renegotiate the deal if you can't make the commitment.

How will you move past barriers? *Create a plan for continuation of business and personal growth.*

Blank Goal Sheet

1st Goal/Objective

Description:_____

_____

_____

Values:

_____

_____

Anti-values:

_____

_____

Measurement:

Importance: ☐ Essential   ☐ Important   ☐ Desirable

Type: ☐ Long Term Goal ☐ Performance Goal ☐ Meeting Goal

Desired Goal Completion Date:

Growth Steps: Identify possible hurdles, roadblocks, or barriers that may hinder your progress on this goal and how you plan to overcome them.

How will you jump over hurdles?

_____

_____

_____

How will you work around roadblocks?

_____

_____

_____

How will you move past barriers?

_____

_____

_____

_____

Blank Goal Sheet

2nd Goal/Objective

Description:_____

_____

_____

Values:

_____

_____

Anti-values:

_____

_____

Measurement:

Importance: ☐ Essential ☐ Important ☐ Desirable

Type: ☐ Long Term Goal ☐ Performance Goal ☐ Meeting Goal

Desired Goal Completion Date:

Growth Steps: Identify possible hurdles, roadblocks, or barriers that may hinder your progress on this goal and how you plan to overcome them.

How will you jump over hurdles?

_____

_____

_____

How will you work around roadblocks?

_____

_____

_____

How will you move past barriers?

_____

_____

_____

_____

Blank Goal Sheet

3rd Goal/Objective

Description:_____

_____

_____

Values:

_____

_____

Anti-values:

_____

_____

Measurement:

Importance: ☐ Essential   ☐ Important   ☐ Desirable

Type: ☐ Long Term Goal   ☐ Performance Goal   ☐ Meeting Goal

Desired Goal Completion Date:

Growth Steps: Identify possible hurdles, roadblocks, or barriers that may hinder your progress on this goal and how you plan to overcome them.

How will you jump over hurdles?

_____

_____

_____

How will you work around roadblocks?

_____

_____

_____

How will you move past barriers?

_____

_____

_____

_____

Journal

_____

_____

_____

_____

_____

_____

_____

_____

_____

_____

_____

_____

_____

_____

_____

_____

_____

_____

_____

_____

_____

_____

_____

_____

_____
_____
_____
_____
_____
_____
_____
_____
_____
_____
_____
_____
_____
_____
_____
_____
_____
_____
_____
_____
_____
_____
_____
_____
_____

_____

_____

_____

_____

_____

_____

_____

_____

_____

_____

_____

_____

_____

_____

_____

_____

_____

_____

_____

_____

_____

_____

_____

_____

_____

_____

_____

_____

_____

_____
_____
_____
_____
_____
_____
_____
_____
_____
_____
_____
_____
_____
_____
_____
_____
_____
_____
_____
_____
_____
_____
_____
_____
_____
_____
_____

_____

_____

_____

_____

_____

_____

_____

_____

_____

_____

_____

_____

_____

_____

_____

_____

_____

_____

_____

_____

_____

_____

_____

_____

_____

_____

_____

_____

_____

_____

_____

_____

_____

_____

_____

_____

_____

_____

_____

_____

_____

_____

_____

_____

_____

_____

_____

_____

_____

_____

_____

_____

_____

_____

_____

_____

_____

_____

_____

_____

_____

_____

_____

_____

_____

_____

_____

_____

_____

_____

_____

_____

_____

_____

_____

_____

_____

_____

_____

_____

_____

_____

_____

_____

_____

_____

_____

_____

_____

_____

_____

_____

_____

_____

_____

_____

_____

_____

_____

_____

_____

_____

_____

Continue Your Journey

Sometimes during a healing journey the things that come up may be too much for you emotionally. Healing hurts and you may find that you need the care of a professional rather than a friend. If this occurs, your next step may involve a professional like a Licensed Mental Health Counselor, Spiritual Counselor (Pastor or Clergy) or Professional Life Coach.

Life coaching is not a substitute for the services provided by a Licensed Mental Health Counselor. Life Coaches guide you to move forward. Mental Health Counselors help you resolve past issues that affect your current mental and emotional health. Some may not find mental health counseling beneficial, while others do a combination of the two. Including a trained spiritual guide will help you attune the spirit and should be someone who will assist in your personal spiritual growth and healing.

But the biggest part of this journey is about discovering what works best for YOU in your healing journey. Once you do, then you will walk the path best suited for YOU.

Reference

¹Root. (n.d.). Retrieved from https://www.merriam-webster.com/dictionary/root

² Posted by Arborilogical Services, & Services, A. (2009, March 1). The Dangers of Root Disturbance. Retrieved from https://www.arborilogical.com/articles/all-articles/article-repository/2009/march/the-dangers-of-root-disturbance/

³ Truth. (2018, February 20). Understanding the purpose and power of woman - Myles Munroe. Retrieved from https://www.youtube.com/watch?v=GhNCeJItZBc

⁴Failure to Thrive. (n.d.). Retrieved from https://www.hopkinsmedicine.org/health/conditions-and-diseases/failure-to-thrive

⁵Abel, D. (2016, April 11). Here's how to spot a potentially treacherous tree - The Boston Globe. Retrieved from https://www.bostonglobe.com/metro/2016/04/10/how-assess-whether-tree-decaying/PMsTVFNYn9JvVUY8JuATLK/story.html

⁶Cloud, H., & Townsend, J. S. (1996). *The mom factor*. Grand Rapids, Mich: Zondervan Publishing.

⁷Webster's New World College Dictionary, Fourth Edition, MacMacMillanew York 1999

About the Author

Athena Thomas is a Spiritual Life Coach and Founder of The Life Calling Coach. She has a specialty in using vision and purpose to establish a path to purpose, life calling and spiritual growth. She serves as the Endurance Program Director for Women Offering Wealth, a non-profit organization. She is also the founder and facilitator of the Sister Circle Support Group for women, a program for survivors of domestic violence and the Circle of Endurance Open Mic.

She knows the difficulty of managing hardships as she has stumbled through life trials, including raising a son with Autism, overcoming depression, and living with anxiety. She now uses her voice, talents, and coaching programs to help others nurture their roots, re-establish focus, and establish balance in life so they can grow into their life purpose. Her holistic approach in her coaching sessions focuses on the mind, body, and spirit.

She is a published author who has written several articles and maintains two blogs. Her work has been featured in newsletters, blogs, and an anthology. Her story will empower you to succeed, push you to overcome, and inspire you to *Live on Purpose and Not by Accident.*

Made in the USA
Middletown, DE
18 June 2021